THE THREE MUSKETEERS

ALEXANDER DUMAS

Adapted by Dr. Marion Kimberly

GALLERY BOOKS
An Imprint of W. H. Smith Publishers Inc.
112 Madison Avenue
New York City 10016

© 1990 Ediciones B, S.A., Barcelona, Spain

This edition published 1991 by Gallery Books,
an imprint of W.H.Smith Publishers, Inc.,
112 Madison Avenue, New York, New York 10016

ISBN 0-8317-1466-2

Gallery Books are available for bulk purchase for sales
promotions and premium use. For details write or telephone
the Manager of Special Sales, W.H.Smith Publishers, Inc.,
112 Madison Avenue, New York, New York 10016. (212) 532-6600

Produced by Hawk Books Limited, London

Printed in Spain

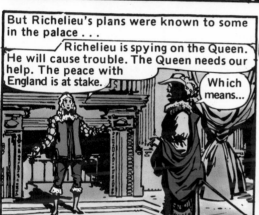

The Gascon's sword might have ended the quarrel then and there, but . . .

Owww!

Thank you, Innkeeper. I'm in a hurry or I'd finish him off right now.

Glad to be of service, sir. Ha! Ha! Ha!

Half an hour later, in a room at the inn . . .

What happened? Oh, I was fighting with that loudmouth when someone hit me.

We must go, My Lady. There's no time to lose. Warn us immediately if the Duke of Buckingham leaves England for France.

Hmmm. There's my loudmouth friend. I wonder who that beautiful woman is . . .

This is the Cardinal's order?

It's for the good of France, My Lady. Buckingham must believe we want peace with England.

It must all be done without the King's knowledge. Go now, I'll return to Paris.

The young Gascon's mind was filled with recent memories . . .

You're a D'Artagnan, my son. Don't run away from danger. I taught you how to use a sword.

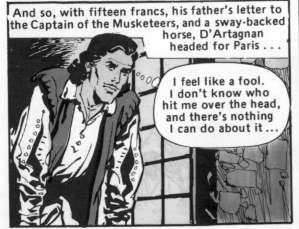

And so, with fifteen francs, his father's letter to the Captain of the Musketeers, and a sway-backed horse, D'Artagnan headed for Paris . . .

I feel like a fool. I don't know who hit me over the head, and there's nothing I can do about it . . .

Meanwhile...

I must hurry to the palace and report to the Cardinal.

D'Artagnan spent the night at the inn, the next morning he was on his way again...

At last, I'm in Paris!

He found a room, and without even washing off the dust of his journey . . .

You're going out right away, sir?

Good lady, I have urgent business in Paris.

He went to see Captain de Treville, commander of the King's Musketeers, and...

Athos, Porthos, Aramis, are you there?

Yes. Captain. Here we are.

The King has ordered me to choose new musketeers from the Cardinal's Guards.

The King's Musketeers, and the Cardinal's Guards . . .

Are bitter enemies, Captain.

Sir, it's not possible.

Captain, a young man named D'Artagnan is waiting to see you.

D'Artagnan? The son of my friend from Gascony?

D'Artagnan gave the Captain his father's letter.

Hmm. So, young man, you want to join the King's Musketeers? I'm glad!

D'Artagnan told Captain de Treville about the man he crossed swords with in Meung.

We'll talk later . . .

The man you fought with spoke to a woman in a coach he called, My Lady?

A very beautiful young woman, sir.

There's no doubt. It was him.

Who is he, Captain? He insulted me and I claim the right to fight for my honour.

That will have to wait, D'Artagnan. You will enter the Royal Academy and learn what a good musketeer needs to know.

Thank you, Captain.

D'Artagnan caught a glimpse of someone through the rear door of the room, and...

What are you staring at young man?

That's the man, sir! This time he's not going to get away!

Oh, excuse me, sir!

Watch where you're going, clown!

Meet me at twelve in the Carmelite's Gardens. I'll teach you to run headlong into people, or my name isn't Athos!

I'll be there.

Hey, where are your eyes, young man?

Excuse me, sir. Excuse me!

If you're not a coward, meet me at the Carmelite's Gardens at noon. I'll teach you a few manners, as sure as my name is Porthos.

Everyone challenges you in this town!

Well, if that was my loudmouthed friend from Meung, he's nowhere in sight, now!

Time passed quickly for D'Artagnan. At noon he headed for the Carmelite's Gardens...

I swear I won't be the first to be killed!

Porthos, what on earth are you doing here?

Exactly what I wanted to ask you, Athos. I came for a duel. And you?

A duel with this man.

It's the same man who came to see the Captain this morning.

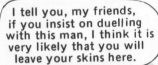

Meanwhile, other things were happening in the palace . . .

Your Majesty, are you feeling ill?

No, I feel well. But...

Constance, I am worried, very worried. The King isn't making any effort to stop Cardinal Richelieu's evil plans for war with England.

Do you realize that Richelieu and his supporters will lead France to disaster, perhaps even war. Neither France nor England wants to fight.

But the Queen didn't see the man standing in the shadows, listening . . .

Come in. I see you have news about the Queen.

You're right, sir. The Queen's maid, Constance, knows how the Queen plans to bring about peace between England and the King.

Hmm. Just as I suspected. I will tell Cardinal Richelieu about the maid immediately.

Meanwhile, let us see what we can do to get more information. In his name, of course! Ha! Ha!

Two days later, a man came to see D'Artagnan...

Open the door, sir. Please let me talk to you.

Excuse me, sir, but your fame as a swordsman has led me to ask you for help.

Who are you? What can I do for you?

My name is Bonacieux. Constance, the Queen's personal maid, is my wife. Someone has taken her, sir.

Mr. Bonacieux, why would they take the Queen's maid?

Constance knows about the Queen's desire for peace with England. The Queen and the Duke of Buckingham are close friends.

They may think they can scare Constance into telling them what the Queen plans to do.

Is there anyone whom you suspect?

Yes, I don't know his name, but there's an evil man in the court . . .

Bonacieux gave D'Artagnan enough details about the mysterious man so that D'Artagnan realized that . . .

It's the man I fought with on my way to Paris. So he's part of this, too!

Trust in me. I'll talk with my friends and see what we can do to find your wife.

Thank you, sir. I'm very grateful for your help.

When Porthos, Athos, and Aramis returned, D'Artagnan told them about Bonacieux's visit.

What do you think of all this, D'Artagnan?

I think Bonacieux is right. The King's enemies want to find out how the Queen plans to keep peace with England.

Suddenly there was a loud knock on the door. Athos opened it, and . . .

Bonacieux!

Help! They're trying to take me!

They suspect Bonacieux and fear that he'll find his wife...

In the King's name this man is under arrest!

Sir, I think it's time we got out of here!

Musketeer, we'll see you again!

Madame, your husband said you had been taken, yet here you are at home.

I escaped last night, sir. They followed me and would have taken me away again but you came.

I'm sorry to tell you that your husband was arrested. I hope we can do something about that.

My poor husband! What will they do to him?

I'll do what I can. Meanwhile, you can stay at the home of a friend of mine. I know you'll be safe there.

D'Artagnan left Constance in a house that Porthos had taken in the same neighbourhood. Later, he met his friends who . . .

I see the evil hand of the Cardinal's supporters in all this. But what are they after?

Don't you see, Athos?

The Cardinal wants some proof of the Queen's guilt. She is the only one who opposes his ideas.

That evening, Porthos' servant, Mousqueton . . .

Sir, Mr. D'Artagnan...

What's happened? Where's Porthos?

He sent me here, sir. I overheard a conversation at the palace. I know what the Cardinal's men want to do . . .

What is it, Mousqueton?

Lady de Winter was sent to London with a false letter from the Queen inviting the Duke to come to Paris. They mean to harm the Queen.

On hearing the words, "Lady de Winter," D'Artagnan remembered the woman in the coach at Meung . . .

We must go. There's no time to lose. Warn us immediately if the Duke comes to France.

Mousqueton, it's a trap! They wrote the letter in the Queen's name. They'll catch her with the English Duke and accuse her of being a traitor.

Planchet, we must go!

The Duke of Buckingham may already be in Paris!

It was midnight when . . .

Planchet, we must save the Queen from this trap!

But, sir, do we always have to fight with swords?

Would you fail to serve your Queen, worm?

Mr. D'Artagnan, I will do what I can to help the Queen. It's just that I'm a coward.

The Duke of Buckingham had arrived in Paris and, following the directions in the false letter, had set out for Constance's home . . .

Yes, sir!

You're surprised? As the Queen's maid, you should have known I was coming.

No, sir. I knew nothing of your trip. I am here only by chance.

She told the Duke of her capture and D'Artagnan's rescue, and then . . .

I'm staying at the home of one of the musketeers. I came here to get a few of my own things.

Will you take me to see the Queen? You must know a secret way to her rooms.

Minutes later . . .

Mrs. Bonacieux? But who is the man?

Richelieu's? Could they have taken her again?

After her! I'll take care of the man!

Yes, sir. I'm coming, but he looked to be a dangerous man.

In the King's name, let her go free, or you will die!

But, what's this? I . . .

D'Artagnan! Stop at once, or our cause will be lost!

Constance introduced the Duke of Buckingham and they shook hands...

You are a brave and worthy friend, sir. Thank you.

I'm honoured, sir.

D'Artagnan explained about the false letter and the planned trap. But the Duke insisted on seeing the Queen anyway. An hour later he was shown into Queen Anne's room...

I promise you, sir, I'll do all I can to keep the peace between France and England. I know our people do not want war.

I'd like to give you something as a token that I mean what I say. Just a minute..

The Queen opened her jewel box and....

Take these diamond studs to remember the unfortunate Queen of France, sir. And now, please be on your way.

Richelieu's spy saw and heard everything...

She fell into the trap! I must tell the Cardinal. Buckingham must not leave here alive!

We have her, My Lord! The trap worked just as you planned.

She gave the Duke two diamonds, part of a set of twelve that the King gave to her.

Let the Duke return to England. There is a better way . . .

The diamonds will be proof that the Queen plotted with Buckingham against France.

As for you, go to England immediately and deliver this message to Lady de Winter.

The message was written in the Cardinal's own hand . . .

Lady de Winter—
Go to the next ball the Duke attends. Take two diamond studs from him without his knowing it. Give them to our loyal Vitray.
E. Richelieu

You will bring the two diamonds that the Queen gave to the Duke of Buckingham to me. They will be proof of her guilt.

Vitray left for London. The next day, Bonacieux was brought to Cardinal Richelieu from the Bastille.

My Lord, I don't know why I was arrested, but I'm sure I haven't done anything wrong.

They say you know of secret plots against France, very serious plots.

I see that you are a man of honour, so I am going to set you free.

Here is one hundred francs for the trouble we've caused you. I hope you won't forget our kindness.

One hundred francs! Thank you, sir!

Long live the First Minister!

Now there's a good man, who will work with me if ever I need him.

Later, in his daily talk with the King . . .

This would be a very good time, Sire, for you to have a ball for the nobles of the court. They need to relax and enjoy themselves.

Hmm, you're right, Cardinal.

It would be nice if the Queen would wear the twelve beautifully matched diamonds that you gave to her earlier this year.

A good idea, Cardinal. Such an expensive gift, and I've never seen her wear them.

Richelieu hoped to spring his trap at the ball. The Queen would be caught without two of her diamonds. Then the Cardinal received a letter from London . . .

I now have the two diamonds. But I need money to get back to France. Please send 500 francs. Your loyal, Vitray

Lady de Winter has done well. The Queen will be disgraced. The people will not listen to her.

Meanwhile, the King told his wife about the ball and of his desire for her to wear the set of twelve diamond studs he had given to her.

I am lost! Buckingham has two of the stones in England.

When she was alone . . .

Constance, you're here! I heard that the Cardinal's men had taken you.

It's all over, Your Highness. The Cardinal was very generous to my husband and later set me free also.

The Queen told Constance about the King's request that she wear her diamonds . . .

I gave two of the diamonds to the Duke of Buckingham, I'll be ruined!

When is the ball to be held?

What can I do? Once it is known that I've seen the Duke secretly, the people will believe I have betrayed France.

Let me bring the brave musketeer, D'Artagnan to see you. I'm sure he can help you and I know you can trust him completely.

D'Artagnan and the musketeers! The Cardinal must be told about this, and quickly!

Constance went to D'Artagnan . . .

Here is the money for your journey. You must get the diamonds before they are stolen by the Cardinal's spies.

D'Artagnan, the future of France and her Queen is in your hands.

Fear not, I will do all in my power to help the Queen. The Cardinal's spies will fail.

Later, D'Artagnan, the three musketeers, and their servants left Paris and sped toward the coast . . .

But the Cardinal's men were waiting for them . . .

Look out!

Ahh!

BANG!

Owww!

BANG!

BANG!

Luckily these wounds are not serious.

If we're to cross the Channel tonight, we've got to go on. Bazin will wait here.

D'Artagnan knew his duty was to France. He had to leave his friends behind and go on alone.

Quick, at a gallop, boy!

I have to get a travel permit to sail as soon as possible!

D'Artagnan stopped. It was the Count of Wades, a man close to Richelieu . . .

You are out of luck. I have the only travel permit, and I'm going to use it!

Is that so?

You're just going to have to give it to me. On guard, sir!

By heaven, those who told me about you were too kind, you rude puppy!

I'll carve you in two and send a piece to the Cardinal.

Not so fast!

That's easier said than done, Count. There!

Awww!

With your permission, sir, I'll just take the travel permit.

Whew! My head is ringing!

D'Artagnan sailed across the channel. Arriving in London, he left Planchet at the inn . . .

A Frenchman, D'Artagnan, wants to see you, sir. He says it's urgent.

Yes, I know that brave musketeer. Send him in.

D'Artagnan, is there trouble? How is the Queen?

She's in great danger, sir!

Quickly, D'Artagnan told the Duke of the risk to the Queen if she didn't wear the diamond studs at the ball...

It would mean the end of peace between England and France.

They plan to have Lady de Winter steal the diamond studs from you as proof the Queen is plotting with England against France.

No, it's not possible!

The Duke opened his jewel box and . . .

Gone! They have the studs!

Lady de Winter was to take them from you. Has she . . .

Yes, Lady de Winter was here at the ball only a few days ago. I had no idea . . .

Sir, will you help me stop them from delivering the diamonds to Cardinal Richelieu?

D'Artagnan, it may be too late.

We can't risk it. My diamond cutter shall make two pieces that are exactly like the stolen gems.

I will take them to the Queen.

Meanwhile, in Paris . . .

The palace ball is just four days away. Are you going to attend?

Of course, my dear, I'm looking forward to it.

In the palace...

Your Majesty, I hope the Queen will wear her diamonds. The entire court wants to see them. They are beautiful and will look lovely on her.

You've said that forty times, Cardinal!

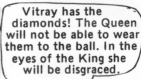

Vitray has the diamonds! The Queen will not be able to wear them to the ball. In the eyes of the King she will be disgraced.

But the Cardinal did not know what D'Artagnan, the Duke of Buckingham, and a diamond expert in London, were doing to save the Queen . . .

Here you are, sir. Just as you wanted them.

Marvelous! D'Artagnan, go to Paris quickly, and give these to the Queen.

Four days later all eyes were turned to the Queen when she entered the ballroom . . .

I have the diamonds. When I show them to the King, the Queen's influence with him will be at an end.

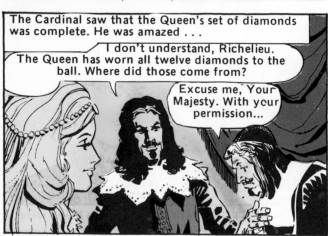

From then on, D'Artagnan was often a visitor in Lady de Winter's home . . .

Has the party started, Kitty? I'm a little late.

Go up, sir. Madame and the other guests are waiting.

I'm sorry I fell in love with him. If he knew the truth about Lady de Winter . . .

That night, after the party, D'Artagnan and Lady de Winter . . .

I have something to tell you. I love you, and want to marry you.

D'Artagnan, you are a fool! Please go now.

No, don't say that! Let me . . .

What are you doing? Let go of my arm . . .

What is that? You . . . You've been branded with a fleur-de-lis!

At that time, people with the fleur-de-lis brand were known criminals!

Now you know my secret! You shall die!

Shocked, D'Artagnan was caught off guard.

Before she could strike . . .

D'Artagnan! Follow me! This way!

Sweet Kitty! You are just in time!

I'm sorry, I wanted to warn you, but I was afraid! Lady de Winter is not her real name.

Come with me! You can't stay here!

Two hours later, they were in the house of the musketeers.

Tomorrow I'll be busy looking for a job away from Paris.

Are you leaving?

"Yes, we should all leave Paris, for a while anyway. We spoiled the Cardinal's game, this time, but he hasn't given up."

"Kitty, don't worry. I'll come back and we'll see each other again."

"I hope so. If not, know that I wish you well."

The next day D'Artagnan was ordered to report to Cardinal Richelieu at the palace . . .

"You'll have to be very careful, my friend."

"Richelieu is a dangerous man."

"Maybe, but so am I."

It was their first meeting . . .

"So you're the famous D'Artagnan. You're a brave man. I'd like you in my private guard. Perhaps a captain . . ."

"I do not see how that would be possible, Cardinal. I do not like this idea of war with England."

"Those who believe such a war is necessary, have been my enemies, sir. I serve with the King's Musketeers."

"You refuse to serve me? Be careful, young man."

But war did come. The English outpost at Rochelle was surrounded. Buckingham brought his men to the island of Re and . . .

"This is Richelieu's war, and it is wrong. I pray it will end quickly."

The French forces prepared to enter the field. D'Artagnan and his three friends were among them . . .

"CHARGE!"

"Long live the King!"

"After them!"

"Charge!"

One night, near the front lines . . .

"Cardinal Richelieu is over there!"

"Is it possible?"

What would Cardinal Richelieu be doing here?

Who knows? He's over there in that farmhouse.

Quietly D'Artagnan entered the farmhouse. Richelieu was talking . . .

Go to London. The Duke of Buckingham is there now. I want you to ask him two things in my name.

First, that he retreat from Rochelle for the sake of the Queen. Second, that he free Lady de Winter, who has made the mistake of becoming a prisoner.

Lady de Winter is an English subject. In order to be set free, she must be pardoned by the Duke. Lady de Winter has been useful to us. I should not like to lose her.

The Cardinal's messenger prepared to leave . . .

The Cardinal is a stubborn man. This war is a disaster.

The Duke will refuse both requests.

¡?

Hello, musketeers. What's happening, gentlemen?

You seem worried, D'Artagnan. Your enemy, Lady de Winter, is a prisoner. As for the Queen and her maid, they're both well.

Do you mean Constance, sir?

I do indeed. The Queen decided to send her to live in a convent so she won't be trapped again. Good luck to you the next time you run into any of my men.

Richelieu returned to Paris. The musketeers went back to the duties of war. The next morning they attacked Rochelle...

This battle wins or loses the war for France!

The battle lasted twenty-four terrible hours . . .

Ahhh!

As it turned out, the battle didn't end the war. Without the help of the British navy, the town of Rochelle was forced to surrender.

HURRAY!

Earlier Richelieu's messenger had arrived in London and arranged to see the Duke of Buckingham . . .

Tell the Cardinal that I won't grant Lady de Winter a pardon. I cannot consider the surrender of Rochelle.

To keep the lady a prisoner is not honorable, sir.

Sir, that is not true. This woman is guilty of many crimes. She is English, but we are not proud of that fact.

Your English troops will not be allowed to stay in France.

Blackguard, that is enough! Get out or I'll have you thrown out!

You'll call no one!

Before the Duke knew what was happening, the man took out a knife and . . .

Ohhh! Scoundrel!

The fool! He asked for it!

Thank you. Who's there?

You're seriously wounded, sir!

It's a letter from France, sir!

I pledge my honour, Lady de Winter will pay for her crimes!

Poor Constance, another victim of Cardinal Richelieu's plans for the glory of France.

The musketeers left the convent later, following Lady de Winter. That night . . .

What town is this, sir?

Armentieres.

Two francs for you. Tell me, have you seen a beautiful young woman with an English accent?

I have, sir. She arrived this afternoon. She is probably staying at the Golden Feather Inn.

The musketeers stabled their horses and . . .

This time there will be no escape for Lady de Winter.

Just a minute, my friends, I beg you!

What Athos told his friends shocked them all . . .

The woman we're about to arrest so that she can be punished, is . . . was . . . my wife!

Yes, it's true. We were married. Afterwards I discovered that she was branded with the fleur-de-lis.

Athos' three friends were silent, knowing the pain he was undergoing...

Later...
Come, we must do our duty!

Ohhh!

Good evening. Did you have a good trip?

You are under arrest. You are accused of killing Constance, the Queen's maid.

You have taken part in evil plots, causing the deaths of good people.

Madame, what do you say?

Filled with fear, this woman who had made her life a chain of crimes, threw herself at D'Artagnan's feet . . .

Pity, sir, I beg you to have pity.

Madame, at least have the dignity to face your punishment.

Minutes later . . .

We'll have to hand her over to the executioner, Athos.

Yes, I know, Aramis. It must be.

Lord, have pity on her.

The Lady de Winter was sentenced to death, and it was soon carried out. A week later, the musketeers reported to Captain de Treville.

The war is over. The King is pleased with the musketeers. But, now it is time to put aside your hatred for Richelieu.

The Cardinal seems to have changed his mind. D'Artagnan, you are to appear before him this afternoon.

My friend, the Captain may be right, but I do not think Richelieu has any love for you.

We'll all go.

Agreed!

When the four arrived at the palace . . .

The order has nothing to do with you. The Cardinal only wants to see D'Artagnan...

I don't like this.

It looks bad!

Richelieu will kill him!

From the palace door, D'Artagnan looked at his friends . . .

It was a long, sad look which he knew could be his last. Then he walked down the hallway . . .

He and the three musketeers had stood back to back in battle. They were brave, loyal men. He was proud to have served King and country with them.

ALL FOR ONE AND ONE FOR ALL. That had been their motto, no matter what happened.

For France and the King!

How would it end? Now he would find out . . .

Ah, D'Artagnan, come in.

You are about to be arrested on my orders. You are accused of working against France, against me, and...

Sir, I have never betrayed France. May I tell you who betrayed France?

It was a woman branded with the fleur-de-lis, a criminal. She murdered the Queen's maid, and is the one who accused me of plotting against my country.

I am speaking of Lady de Winter, sir. She is English, and that's not her real name, but you trusted her.

D'Artagnan, if all you say is true, I'll see to it that she's punished.

That's been done, sir.

Richelieu was angry when he was told about the execution of Lady de Winter..

So you and your friends decided to be the judges and ignore us here in Paris?

It is my painful duty to tell you that countless crimes were carried out by her, in your name. We have proof of it all, sir.

As Richelieu listened, his anger was replaced by sadness. After a while the Cardinal raised his head and . . .

I see, D'Artagnan. I know your friends are outside, ready to fight, if you're not set free. True?

Yes, my friends are waiting for me.

Richelieu rang a bell and . . .

Send Vitray in immediately.

Right away, sir.

It's a real shame, that among my men there's not one like you. I wish there were...

Now he'll give my death sentence...

Ah, Vitray. I want you to . . .

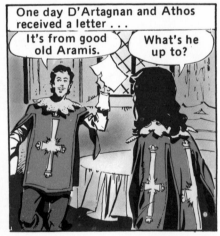

THE END